Chef Leel | Executive Chef
Email | info@chefleel.com
Patreon | thechefleel
Instagram | thechefleel
Twitter | thechefleel
Tik Tok | thechefleel
Youtube | Chef Leel

VEGINNERS

by Jaleel Malik Hasan

contents

Veginners | A beginner's guide to a healthier lifestyle

Introduction

Food is all around us. Food is love. Food is family. Food is nourishment. Food is longevity. Food is information. These are the consequences of food. Anything else we consume is waste.

For Chef Leel (me), food has always been the bridge between love and life. As a child, food was always a medium for bringing the family together. We enjoyed large family gatherings and homemade dishes, from in-house casseroles to triple-layered frosted cakes and pecan pies. Like most Aboriginal American families, we could not enjoy enough Crisco fried, crisp battered, breaded chicken, canned soda (pop), ice cream, and cookies. These are the foods that brought us together. As long as our stomachs were filled, so were our hearts. That's what real food does, so we've been taught.

Real food nourishes the human body and revitalizes the cells of the human body. Our dietary regimen is designed to support the body's preliminary healing capacity. While Aboriginal American families perpetually adopt the regimen of the standard American diet (SAD), we also inherit the habits, ideologies, and illnesses that result from consuming foods of this diet. Our communities are plagued by diabetes, high blood pressure, cancer, heart disease, stroke, sickle cell anemia, and other ailments resulting from a lack of proper nutrition. Just as our traditional meals have brought us together, these same traditions, or habits, have also divided us and disrupted our sustenance of life, longevity, and harmony.

Food is the bridge between love and life. With the proper nutrition, we will promote the longevity of health and wellness and continue to enjoy the love, laughter, and unity within our local and global communities of family, friends, and loved ones. In *Veginners*, Chef Leel provides healthy, tasty recipes that bring and keep the family together. Cooking "The Chef Leel Way" is culinary artistry inspired by the African bio-mineral balance, a methodology provided by our late ancestor, Dr. Alfredo "Sebi" Bowman. Since this methodology has been proven to support the recovery of food-related illnesses, the coming recipes use only foods listed on *Dr. Sebi's Nutritional Guide.*

What it means to be "Vegan"

Living a healthier lifestyle could be viewed as a natural desire. To maximize our capacity to love, socialize, communicate, collaborate, and innovate, we need to be healthy. As we introduce more technology into our global society, build more homes and concrete structures, and continue to grow as a population, we are also less inclined to preserve agriculture and farmland with integrity. These factors result in the necessity for us, as a species, to evolve our perpetual consuming habits, more specifically, what and how we eat.

The term vegan, or the vegan practice, is a derivative of vegetarian or vegetarianism. A vegetarian is a person who does not consume meat or animal flesh, although vegetarians do generally eat dairy and eggs. The term vegan is said to have been coined by an Englishman named Donald Watson. Born in the United Kingdom, Watson became a vegetarian at fourteen years old. Within eighteen years, Watson realized the industry of dairy production was unethical. He came to understand that the output of dairy-based foods and products made it necessary to exploit and slaughter animals inhumanely. In November 1944, Watson evolved the practice of vegetarianism by creating the term "vegan" to describe any person or group of people who abstain from consuming meat, dairy, and eggs. Watson would eventually refine the vegan movement and the concept of veganism to object to the harm of any living creature. Now, more than 75.3 million people make up the world's vegan population. Many continue in the development and innovation of the vegan philosophy.

According to a recent study from the Vegetarian Research Group, 68% of the study participants indicated that they became vegan to protect animals. While 69% of the participants indicated they are vegan to attain and maintain health, today's vegan population seems to be primarily concerned with protecting animals or living creatures and following a more strict dietary practice. For me, veganism is more than a modification to one's diet; it's about much more than contributing to the salvation of nonhuman animals. A transition into veganism is a lifestyle change. It is not a diet; it is a lifestyle. Not merely a difference in what we eat, but an evolution in what we consume internally and externally, what we consume through our skin, through our eyes, through our ears, from our peers, from our respective environments, households, and institutions. Each factor in our overall health and stability. Strong emphasis on "our." Our physical strength, our mental stability, and our spiritual peace.

"Vegan" has become slang, more of a common term to describe one who does not eat meat, dairy, or eggs, or animal byproducts. But what is vegan at its core? Vegan is a choice. A choice to commit to the ongoing transformation, experience, and practice of self-love, self-awareness, and self-development. Why should we consider veganism? To attain and sustain success, one must acquire longevity, wealth. Our ability to reap our harvest is a repercussion of what we consume. A transition into a vegan lifestyle is a step towards maximizing our potential in every capacity.

Humans Plant, Plants Human

The human body's fundamental building blocks are carbon, hydrogen, oxygen, nitrogen, calcium, and phosphorous. Other elements present in the body are found in smaller quantities, and some have yet to illustrate any special, essential functions. The human body uses carbohydrates, fats, and proteins that store and uses energy to carry out the body's primary functions. Energy is primarily used via carbohydrates, which are found mainly in fruits, vegetables, and grains. Fats are said to be the body's secondary energy source, although fats carry the most energy. Healthy fats can be found in plants, including avocados, coconuts, nuts, and seeds. Proteins regulate cell growth, tissue repair and support immune function. Protein-rich plant foods include amaranth, quinoa, hemp seeds, beans, and rice. Plant foods containing proteins should be consumed in a variety to satisfy the blockchain of complete proteins.

As some of the earliest life forms on Earth, plants are a prerequisite to most life forms, current and extinct. According to fossil records, land plants appeared on Earth some 450 to 500 million years ago, predating humans by mega-years. Even with this vast time difference of first appearances on Earth, plants and humans maintain a symbiotic relationship. Through a process known as photosynthesis, green plants make their food to grow and sustain life. Photosynthesis is when a plant uses the energy of sunlight to convert water and carbon dioxide into glucose (food for the plant) while releasing oxygen into the atmosphere.

The human body uses sunlight to produce Vitamin D to absorb calcium and phosphorous and support the function of the immune system, bones, and blood cells. The potential of the human body's overall function is dictated by the body's capacity to supply itself with oxygen. When humans breathe, our lungs deliver oxygen to the blood cells. Carbon Dioxide is the waste of this process, which we remove from our bodies when we exhale. Simultaneously, plants use that carbon dioxide and, in return, supply us with oxygen. Chlorophyll is the molecule in plants that harvests the energy of the sun. Hemoglobin (human blood) is a protein in the red blood cells responsible for transporting oxygen throughout the human body. The chemical structure of chlorophyll in plants and hemoglobin in humans is identical, with magnesium at the center of the chlorophyll molecule and iron at the center of the hemoglobin molecule. These unique relationships between plants and humans are the constituents for plants and animals to grow and advance.

To sustain life on this planet, plants are necessary for supplying food for all animals, directly and indirectly; as the volume of plant life decreases, animals' food and oxygen supply decreases. Almost the entire global population makes up the percentage of people who consume meat. Each year, the world population increases and, with it, the demand for meat increases. To produce more meat, more energy and water are required. Meat production contributes to the excess of greenhouse gas emissions. Greenhouse gases absorb the power of the sun and redirect it back to the Earth as heat. This manufactures the greenhouse effect, which produces additional heat to the Earth's surface and oceans, causing weather extremities, climate change, air pollution, and low crop and plant growth. Nearly 80% of global agricultural land is used to produce meat resulting in deforestation, animal extinction, less oxygen, and less space for the growing population. Meat, dairy, and eggs require more water than the production of any other food source on the planet. Almost half of the water consumed globally is used to grow food for livestock. Remember, the demand for meat is increasing, so livestock needs are increasing, resulting in the continuous decrease in overall available freshwater.

      The general population often consumes meat, dairy, eggs, or animal byproducts without understanding how that consumption adversely affects our ecosystem and our health. How we choose to live will always have external and internal consequences. According to the World Health Organization, the leading causes of death globally are heart disease, stroke, diabetes, and respiratory-related illnesses. These diseases are all related to diet, nutrition, and exercise. The consumption of meat, dairy, and eggs can have a range of short-term and long-term effects on the human body. Consuming excess saturated fat induces the build-up of cholesterol in the arteries, which restricts blood flow. Cholesterol is a fat synthesized by the liver and transported to the bloodstream to make hormones, Vitamin D, and support digestion. Meat, milk, eggs, and cheese are all abundant in saturated fats. These foods are the catalyst to heart disease, the world's leading cause of death.

      Contrary to popular belief, chicken is of the most toxic of meats. Chickens are being dosed with arsenic carrying antibiotics resulting in the dramatically increased risks of cancer, high blood pressure, heart attacks, and circulatory disease. The result of cooking chicken or any other meat is the generation of carcinogens. Carcinogens are substances or radiation that cause cancer. The amino acids and protein from meat, dairy, and eggs can also overstimulate the central regulator of metabolism in mammals. This protein/regulator is responsible for cell growth and cell division. The overexpression of this protein leads to human diseases, including diabetes, cancer, and obesity. Being intentional with the foods we ingest allows us to be more autonomous in managing our overall health status.

      The connection between plants and humans is a testament to humans' obligation to practice a plant-based lifestyle. Plants are the foundational food source for all animals. A carnivore can receive its nutrients from plants indirectly. The same is true with omnivores in terms of their meat consumption. Humans are anatomically designed to digest water-soluble foods. It takes up to two days to fully digest meat. Think of meat as the "middle man" between you and your nourishment. Most of the meat consumed by the average person was an animal that ate plants. Through meat, we are supplied with nutrition because the source of nutrition is in the plants.

      In society, we often pass through several tolls to receive what we deem as a necessity. We usually do this for the sake of convenience. When we go through the "middle man," the product we've demanded is often diluted in value. Fast food is such a convenience, but still just another process of receiving a product whose original value has diminished. I can order a salad from a restaurant, but the "middle man" decides the proportion of each ingredient that composes the salad. How much dressing you'll get, where the ingredients are sourced from, the price of the meal. A vegan lifestyle is a choice and practice of taking control of your life and what you put in your body and on your body. What you feed your mind, what you feed your spirit and your soul. You can manage the quality of the food you buy. Where it comes from, how it is grown or nurtured. You can decide how much sauce you get with your entree, how much dip you get with your chip. The responsibility is yours.

We are deceived by the illusion that healthy eating is a costly lifestyle change. Many of us assume that plant-eating is more expensive than deadly eating. Compared to the price of ground beef, we can easily conclude which one costs less. We have to ask ourselves what the cost of ground beef actually is... what the cost of any of our favorite foods is. If what you ingest obstructs the body's ability to heal, then what is the actual expense of the transaction. Short-term gratification is a plague in our communities. Satisfying a craving is often prioritized above nourishment. This is because we haven't acknowledged our addictions to food.

Our connection to plants is multi-faceted, but we inevitably build a rapport with whatever we ingest, mainly food. The relationship we have with our food is proportional to the status of our overall health. Some of us have built a toxic relationship with our bodies. We eat junk food when we're frustrated to cope with our discomfort—eating chocolate, candy, cookies, and ice cream while failing to acknowledge when we're eating out of emotion. We punish ourselves physically, and, in return, that energy is reciprocated as diabetes, heart disease, or cancer. The characteristics of your diet begin to translate into your daily interactions. A toxic relationship with your food, with your body, with yourself, influences your social connections. What goes inside of your body dictates the structure of your vessel and its occupying force. Building a healthy relationship with your food constructs harmony with and in yourself, the practice of self-love. By nurturing your body, you can reward yourself. Eating plants to grow more plants to receive more oxygen to receive more life. More plants translate to more land, which translates to more food and water, and more animals, which translates to a stable ecosystem, translating to a more sustainable overall global health. A plant food lifestyle is the most impactful lifestyle choice that compliments the individual and the integrated collective of life on Earth.

Notes

Today is a Gift

Life is a peculiar experience unique to every individual and every living organism. All life forms have the innate desire to evolve. We want to innovate our current practices to increase and maximize our potential. There is no way to pinpoint when the process of development and advancement begins. It could start with abstinence. The process could even begin with an idea. Knowing when is just as important as it is not. It is more important to know now. Now is the present moment. The future will eventually be the present moment, and the past has already been the present. All forms of time are intertwined with right now. Evolution is homogeneous with change. Many of us are intimidated by the idea of change. We know that change requires us to mold a new mentality and a new environment. Change typically carries a discouraging connotation because it interrupts routines and disrupts comfort. The beauty of change is that it guarantees different results. Further results can mean progression or decline. That is why right now is the best moment for evolution because continuing the routine and perpetuating revolving habits omits the risk of moving backward and denies the opportunity to move forward.

Every day, the demand for meat increases. This means meat production will continue to increase as it has more than doubled in the last thirty-plus years. Remember, to produce more meat, dairy, and eggs, more water, land, and energy are required than that of any other food source. More plants translate to more oxygen. More plants translate to more land. More plants translate to more energy. As the demand for produce increases, the necessity of growing more plants will increase. Adjusting your lifestyle to support your health ultimately contributes to Earth's health and its inhabitants. The Universe (consciousness, source, spirit, etc.) runs on a cyclical series of transactions. Transactions allow for the transfer of energy to maintain equilibrium in a body. Our superficial structures are built on this concept. If you want to buy a house, the transaction requires currency. Currency involves an exchange of products or services. Services require an exchange of energy. Energy requires food. Food is energy. In our ecosystem, energy is transferred through producers, consumers, and de-composers. This is the natural balance preserved by living organisms. When we go against this balance, we deplete energy from the Universe or diverse/dual-versal system.

We say that time is money, but time is energy. We exert, extend, and receive energy over periods. At that same time, we build, we create, we change, we grow, we construct, and we deconstruct. We fashion our life experiences with our energy and the energy around us. This is why health is wealth. Wealth represents the longevity of our labor's fruits, and health is the vehicle to create and maintain wealth.

Start making daily efforts to eat and live more healthily right now, at this moment. Today is a gift because all you have is the present. You decide what's in it, how it's wrapped, and what you'll do with it. Be intentional and make the best of it. You can materialize anything you imagine. You have to seize the gift of right now.

Thoughts and Affirmations

Commit to Yourself

For you to achieve success, you must first be able to define success. What is success for you? Knowing what success is for you allows you to articulate a measurable goal. If success means taking care of yourself and your family, then economic sovereignty or financial freedom could be a goal for you. Once you've specified your goal, you'll need to construct a plan to accomplish the goal. A long-term goal is made up of the succession of short-term goals. Your program should be designed to complete micro-goals; daily, weekly, or monthly. To follow through on your plan, you'll have to practice the quintessential discipline required to achieve your success. Your vocation, your plan, and your success are all governed by your commitment. A commitment can last as long as the process for accomplishing your goals, or it can last a lifetime. Each day, you get the opportunity to evolve from your past self.

Tomorrow, you can be more robust, more agile, more energetic, more wealthy, more compassionate, whatever you strive for. Progression is the product of commitment and action. Imagine that you'll make daily efforts to develop and improve your physical, mental, and spiritual condition for the rest of your life. Your efforts will not be reduced to a burden because you will reap the rewards of your commitment recurrently. Once you've made your commitment, you'll begin to formulate a goal-oriented routine that makes acquiring success inevitable. Building your discipline requires you to measure where you're at and where you're trying to go.

Quality of health is obligatory to quality of life. In our society, our overall health is strongly influenced by the standard American diet (SAD). The SAD generally consists of red meats, white meats, fish, seafood; dairy, eggs; processed foods and processed sugars; and fast foods and fountain drinks. Knowing where you fall within this stipulation is how you will gauge your transition into veganism or a more healthy lifestyle. Your discipline will stem from your commitment to this process. Your process should be unique to you but should maintain a barometer of high-quality results. You are making changes to make a change in your life. There is no universal method for transitioning into a vegan lifestyle. Just know that you are capable and have resources to support you.

Since veganism constitutes the abstinence of meat, dairy, eggs, and animal byproducts, you'll want to dramatically reduce and eliminate your consumption of these foods and products derived from meat, dairy, eggs, or any animal byproduct. One strategy would be to make small changes to your everyday meals. You could try removing or substituting meat once a week. Great plant substitutes for meat are mushrooms in their variety. Portobello, white mushrooms, or crimini mushrooms can be cooked to resemble a beef-like experience. Oyster mushrooms are versatile in texture and can be manipulated to mimic almost any meat, chiefly chicken or fish. Lobster mushrooms get their name due to their palatable resemblance to lobster and crab meat. Similarly, chicken of the woods mushrooms distinctly has a texture and consistency of chicken.

Another method would be to eliminate one meat at a time each day, week, or month. In my experience, most people expel red meats first. It may be more or less challenging to remove one meat or another, depending on your experience. It's less important to focus on which strategy will be "easiest" but more imperative to invest in the end goal. Choosing to take steps toward a healthier lifestyle is an investment in your future, not a sacrifice in your present. Committing to the long-term outcomes will see you through any milestone. If someone who loves chicken removes chicken from their dietary provisions, their transition will accelerate as they've overcome the more difficult obstacle course. Similarly, success can be achieved by eliminating any meat first or last. If you get stuck in your meat removal process, remember the effects of meat consumption on your body, health, environment, and the planet.

The idea of meat, the appearance, and the smell of meat might become less and less appealing when you know how it's processed and its adverse effects. The key is to convert your lifestyle gradually. All we have is right now, so urgency is vital. After altogether removing meat, including fish and seafood, it's time to relinquish the dairy. That includes milk, eggs, cheese, and any products derived from or related to dairy. From your diet/lifestyle, dairy can be removed simultaneously with meat. Every day that passes is another opportunity to heal ourselves and heal others. Urgency is vital. However, the destination is more important than the speed of the vehicle.

Furthermore, place more emphasis on the journey above the objective. That will ground you in the present, the most crucial moment in time. Create a pact with yourself that compliments you, and demands holding yourself to high expectations.

To remove dairy from your diet entirely, you may want to follow the same process for removing the meat. There are even more alternatives to dairy-based products. All traditional and conventional kinds of milk can be replaced with nut or seed milk. Nut and seed milk are widely accessible. Most conveniently, nut and seed milk can be made at home with a blender and a strainer. Likewise, nuts or seeds can be used to make cheese alternatives. Cheese seems to be the most significant challenge for those who have made it to vegetarianism. The not-so-secret about cheese is that it contains a protein called casein. The shorter strings in its amino acid chain are casomorphins. These are morphine-like receptors that attach to the opiate receptors in your brain. Essentially, cheese is an opioid. You are less inclined to cheese for its taste and texture and more inclined to cheese because you've built an addiction. To break a habit (addiction), limiting contact or potential contact with the substance can be best. When you shop, avoid the entire dairy section. In your home, remove all meat and dairy products or finish them off with the intent of replacing your detrimental habits with new healthy ones. All of our circumstances are different, so you must activate your critical thinking skills. You alone are enough to change your circumstances. Integrity is defined as adherence to moral and ethical principles, soundness of moral character; honesty; the state of being whole, entire, or undiminished. Exemplify impeccable integrity and commit to yourself!

Goals and Commitments

I am grateful that I have already accomplished:

_____

_____

_____

_____

_____

_____

I am currently working towards:

_____

_____

_____

_____

_____

_____

_____

_____

I will succeed in acquiring the above desires by committing to:

_____

_____

_____

_____

_____

_____

_____

I know that I am capable of succeeding because:

_____

_____

_____

_____

Sample Transition Tracker

Natural Spring Water checklist:

_x_ 16oz _x_ 16oz _x_ 16oz _x_ 16oz

_x_ 16oz _x_ 16oz _x_ 16oz ___16oz

Bonus: ___8oz ___8oz ___8oz

Non-water beverages I usually have:

Coffee   frappuccino   milkshake

soda   slushee   juice

What I would usually eat today:
Breakfast

Fried eggs   bacon   bagel w/

cream cheese   cereal   pizza

bacon egg & cheese on a roll

Lunch

Turkey sandwich   chicken wrap

cheeseburger   loaded fries

chicken salad   ramen

Dinner

Chicken alfredo   turkey dinner

chicken sandwich w/ fries

gumbo   shrimp scampi

Snacks

Chips   candy   ice cream

cookies   doughnuts   chocolate

Healthy options for today:

Water   herbal tea   organic juice

fresh smoothie   vegan milkshake

Healthier alternatives for today:
Breakfast

Oatmeal   porridge   whole grain-

pancakes   fruit salad   garbanzo-

bean eggs   watermelon   juice

Lunch

Veggie sandwich   veggie wrap

smoothie   veggie "burger"

chipotle bowl   plant-based brunch

Dinner

Veggie pizza   veggie lasagna

kamut alfredo   veggie tacos

veggie stir fry   deluxe salad

Snacks

Mango slices   guac   dates/nuts

fruit leather   kale chips   granola

Challenges, solutions, and highlights for today:

Today, I was challenged with drinking a whole gallon of water. I can start drinking water earlier or even substituting water for breakfast. Still, I drank more than yesterday. Also, I completed my day eating plant-based for breakfast and lunch. Progress is worth celebrating! Chicken Fried Mushrooms tomorrow?

Transition Tracker (Reusable)

Natural Spring Water checklist:

___16oz ___16oz ___16oz ___16oz

___16oz ___16oz ___16oz ___16oz

Bonus: ___8oz ___8oz ___8oz

Non-water beverages I usually have:

_____

_____

What I would usually eat today:
Breakfast

_____

_____

_____

Lunch

_____

_____

_____

Dinner

_____

_____

_____

Snacks

_____

_____

Healthier options for today:

_____

_____

Healthier alternatives for today:
Breakfast

_____

_____

_____

Lunch

_____

_____

_____

Dinner

_____

_____

_____

Snacks

_____

_____

Challenges, solutions, and highlights for today:

_____

_____

_____

_____

Transition Tracker (Reusable)

Natural Spring Water checklist:

___16oz   ___16oz   ___16oz   ___16oz

___16oz   ___16oz   ___16oz   ___16oz

Bonus: ___8oz   ___8oz   ___8oz

Non-water beverages I usually have:	Healthier options for today:
_____	_____
_____	_____

What I would usually eat today:	Healthier alternatives for today:
Breakfast	Breakfast
_____	_____
_____	_____
Lunch	Lunch
_____	_____
_____	_____
Dinner	Dinner
_____	_____
_____	_____
Snacks	Snacks
_____	_____

Challenges, solutions, and highlights for today:

_____

_____

_____

_____

Transition Tracker (Reusable)

Natural Spring Water checklist:

___16oz   ___16oz   ___16oz   ___16oz

___16oz   ___16oz   ___16oz   ___16oz

Bonus: ___8oz   ___8oz   ___8oz

Non-water beverages I usually have:

_____

_____

What I would usually eat today:
Breakfast

_____

_____

_____

Lunch

_____

_____

_____

Dinner

_____

_____

_____

Snacks

_____

_____

Healthier options for today:

_____

_____

Healthier alternatives for today:
Breakfast

_____

_____

_____

Lunch

_____

_____

_____

Dinner

_____

_____

_____

Snacks

_____

_____

Challenges, solutions, and highlights for today:

_____

_____

_____

_____

Transition Tracker (Reusable)

Natural Spring Water checklist:

___16oz ___16oz ___16oz ___16oz

___16oz ___16oz ___16oz ___16oz

Bonus: ___8oz ___8oz ___8oz

Non-water beverages I usually have:

_____

_____

What I would usually eat today:
Breakfast

_____

_____

_____

Lunch

_____

_____

_____

Dinner

_____

_____

_____

Snacks

_____

_____

Healthier options for today:

_____

_____

Healthier alternatives for today:
Breakfast

_____

_____

_____

Lunch

_____

_____

_____

Dinner

_____

_____

_____

Snacks

_____

_____

Challenges, solutions, and highlights for today:

_____

_____

_____

_____

Transition Tracker (Reusable)

Natural Spring Water checklist:

___16oz ___16oz ___16oz ___16oz

___16oz ___16oz ___16oz ___16oz

Bonus: ___8oz ___8oz ___8oz

Non-water beverages I usually have:

_____

_____

What I would usually eat today:
Breakfast

_____

_____

Lunch

_____

_____

Dinner

_____

_____

Snacks

_____

_____

Healthier options for today:

_____

_____

Healthier alternatives for today:
Breakfast

_____

_____

Lunch

_____

_____

Dinner

_____

_____

Snacks

_____

_____

Challenges, solutions, and highlights for today:

_____

_____

_____

_____

Transition Tracker (Reusable)

Natural Spring Water checklist:

___16oz ___16oz ___16oz ___16oz

___16oz ___16oz ___16oz ___16oz

Bonus: ___8oz ___8oz ___8oz

Non-water beverages I usually have:

_____

_____

What I would usually eat today:
Breakfast

_____

_____

_____

Lunch

_____

_____

Dinner

_____

_____

Snacks

_____

_____

Healthier options for today:

_____

_____

Healthier alternatives for today:
Breakfast

_____

_____

_____

Lunch

_____

_____

Dinner

_____

_____

Snacks

_____

_____

Challenges, solutions, and highlights for today:

_____

_____

_____

_____

Transition Tracker (Reusable)

Natural Spring Water checklist:

___16oz ___16oz ___16oz ___16oz

___16oz ___16oz ___16oz ___16oz

Bonus: ___8oz ___8oz ___8oz

Non-water beverages I usually have:

_____

_____

Healthier options for today:

_____

_____

What I would usually eat today:
Breakfast

_____

_____

_____

Healthier alternatives for today:
Breakfast

_____

_____

_____

Lunch

_____

_____

Lunch

_____

_____

Dinner

_____

_____

Dinner

_____

_____

Snacks

_____

_____

Snacks

_____

_____

Challenges, solutions, and highlights for today:

_____

_____

_____

_____

RECIPES

Chef Leel's Quinoa Cakes

Servings:
Yields 6 cakes

Equipment:
Blender   Mixing Bowl
Whisk   Spoon   Skillet
Spatula

Ingredients:
1 cup quinoa flour
1/2 cup garbanzo flour
3 baby bananas
3/4 tsp sea salt
1 1/2 cup sparkling water
1/2 tbsp grapeseed oil
Coconut oil
Agave/ date syrup

Growing up, the sensation of waking up to the aroma of Grandma's homemade pancakes coming off of the iron skillet was a euphoric one. I was always motivated to start my day early and complete any task that would bring me closer to savoring Grandma's pancakes. That experience still lives in Chef Leel's kitchen but with ingredients suitable for long-lasting health.

Procedure:

1. Add baby bananas, garbanzo flour, and 1/2 cup sparkling water to blender. Blend on high for 30 seconds to make wet batter.
2. In a mixing bowl, mix quinoa flour and sea salt.
3. Add wet batter and remaining sparkling water to dry batter. Fold in to completely combine.
4. Preheat skillet to medium-high heat. Coat with 1 tbsp grapeseed oil.
5. Pour batter into skillet to form 6 inch cakes. Allow edges to cook and wait for bubbles to appear. Flip and cook for 20 seconds. Remove from skillet.
6. Lather cakes with coconut oil, top with agave or date syrup, serve, and enjoy.

Chef Leel's Quinoa Cakes are great with assorted berries, or with *Chef Leel's Chicken Fried Mushrooms*, or even as a large stack of fluffy sweetness.

Chef Leel's Electric Guac

Servings:
Serves 2-4

Equipment:

Mixing Bowl	Whisk
Knife	Fork	Spoon

Ingredients:
2 large avocados
1 plum tomato (diced)
1/2 red onion (diced)
1 1/2 tbsp key lime juice
3/4 tsp sea salt
1/2 tsp onion powder
1/8 tsp african bird pepper

As a kid, I was terrified of guacamole. I watched movies with scenes of women going out to enjoy a spa day. Most times, their faces would be covered with almost like an avocado puree. They would also have cucumbers over their eyes. I remember one woman taking the cucumber off her eye and scooping up some of the avocado on her face. Now, I know why. Avocado is that versatile fruit containing healthy fats, and it pairs well with just about anything. Try using it *The Chef Leel Way* and enjoy the snack that's perfect for any time of the day.

Procedure:

1. Add key lime juice, sea salt, onion powder, and african bird pepper to a small mixing bowl. Whisk to fully combine. Set aside.
2. Remove skin and seed from avocados. Add to mixing bowl with wet ingredients.
3. Mash Avocados in the mixing bowl until the mixture is coarse and slightly chunky.
4. Fold in diced plum tomato and diced red onion until fully combined. Serve and Enjoy.

Chef Leel's Electric Guac is a great addition to *Chef Leel's Nachos*, tacos, wraps, and salads. It can also be scooped up with *Chef Leel's Spelt Tortilla Chips*, or even with raw bell pepper slices.

Chef Leel's Ground Shroom

Servings:
Serves 2-4

Equipment:
Spatula   Skillet
Food Processor

Ingredients:
6 oz portobello mushrooms (chopped)
2 cups walnuts (soaked overnight)
t tsp sea salt
1 tsp coriander
1/2 tsp onion powder
1/4 tsp savory
1/4 tsp achiote

Chef Leel's Ground Shroom is like the ground beef or ground turkey of plants. We often obliged in quick meals for time and financial convenience throughout my middle school and high school years. A typical meal was hamburger helper. We always used ground beef as the protein. This was almost like a staple in my household, as my mom perfected the recipe and still added her own style to it. Once I learned to do the same, I carried the tradition into my adulthood. *Chef Leel's Ground Shroom* can create the same experience and uses plants to help the cow and help you.

Procedure:

1. Add mushrooms, walnuts, and dry ingredients to food processor.
2. Pulse 9-12 times.
3. Preheat skillet to medium-high heat.
4. Transfer mixture to preheated skillet.
5. Cook for 12-14 minutes until moisture has evaporated and mixture has browned. Mix moderately.
6. Remove from heat. Serve. Enjoy.

Chef Leel's Ground Shroom is a great addition to *Chef Leel's Nachos*. This mixture can be added to pizzas, tacos, burritos, spaghetti and pastas, salads, sandwiches, and veggie wraps.

Chef Leel's Nachos

Equipment:
Large Bowl
Knife   Blender

Servings:
Serves 2-4

Ingredients:
Chef Leel's Spelt Tortilla Chips
4 cups green leaf lettuce (shredded)
2 cups Chef Leel's Ground Shroom
4 plum tomatoes (diced)
1 red onion (diced)
1 hass avocado (mashed)
Chef Leel's Hemp Seed Mayo
1 key lime juice
1/4 cup spring water

I had my first experience working a part-time job after a full school day in my early college years. Of course, this conjured up a huge appetite, and I was already a food junkie. The most convenient and widely available food substance was at fast food and local restaurants as a working college student. It was ideal to stop by a fast-food restaurant before or after work for a quick meal. I used to love picking up a to-go bowl of nachos with extra beef, sour cream, and jalapenos. Even if Nachos were being served in the cafeteria, I would indulge. *Chef Leel's Nachos* are the healthy alternative that has all the crunch, flavor, and diversity.

Procedure:

1. In a blender, add *Chef Leel's Hemp Seed Mayo*, juice of 1 key lime, and 1/4 cup spring water. Blend on high for 20 seconds. Transfer to a sauce bottle or glass jar.
2. In a large bowl, build your nacho tower by layering the ingredients sequentially.
3. Fill the bowl with *Chef Leel's Spelt Tortilla Chips*.
4. Next, add a layer of shredded green leaf lettuce.
5. On top of the lettuce, add 2 cups of *Chef Leel's Ground Shroom* and top with diced red onions and plum tomatoes.
6. In a separate bowl, mash a large avocado. Add to the top of the tower.
7. Drizzle mixture from step 1 over nacho tower. Serve. Enjoy.

Chef Leel's Nachos is the perfect homemade appetizer to awaken your appetite. You can make a smaller portion and eat this as an afternoon snack, or make a larger portion and share it with family and friends. Also, try adding *Chef Leel's Brazil Nut Cheddar* for a more traditional style nacho bowl.

Chef Leel's Perfect Quinoa

Servings:
Serves 1-2

Equipment:
Strainer Sauce Pot
Mixing Spoon

Ingredients:
2 cups quinoa (soaked overnight)
3 cups spring water
1/2 tbsp onion powder
1 tsp sea salt
1/8 tsp ginger powder
1/8 tsp basil
1/8 tsp african bird pepper
2 tsp coconut oil

White rice was a staple in my household. The adults would cook it with salt and other spices. I loved the sweet version with salted butter and sugar. The rice would start to stick together as I stirred it. We would pair it with almost anything, but I could eat it all by itself. As I matured, I began to steer towards the adult version. As I began to adopt a healthier lifestyle, I began developing relationships with the ancient grains. Soon enough, *Chef Leel's Perfect Quinoa* was born. An all-new nutty experience with all the nutritional value.

Procedure:

1. Strain and rinse soaked quinoa with distilled or spring water. Add to a sauce pot then cover with 3 cups spring water.
2. Bring pot to a boil. Reduce heat to a rolling boil. Cook for two minutes uncovered.
3. Remove from heat and strain excess water from pot.
4. Add remaining ingredients to quinoa and mix well. Cover for 10 minutes. Serve. Enjoy.

Chef Leel's Perfect Quinoa pairs well with just about any dish. Try adding it to *Chef Leel's Raw Garden Salad*. Enjoy it in a veggie wrap, in a stew, or in a bowl all by itself.

Chef Leel's Perfect Wild Rice

Servings:
Serves 1-2

Equipment:
Strainer   Sauce Pot
Mixing Spoon

Ingredients:
2 cups wild rice (soaked overnight)
8 cups spring water
2 1/4 tsp sea salt
2 tsp onion powder
1/2 tsp ginger powder
1/4 tsp oregano
1/8 tsp african bird pepper
1/2 tbsp grapeseed oil

Wild rice is a grain commonly found in mixes of rice and different grains. Certain southern-style foods incorporate wild rice fairly often. My mother loved that southern-style New Orleans taste. We ate a lot of dirty rice and jambalaya. The food was always spicy. After I introduced wild rice into my pallet, I thought I had never had it before. On the contrary, I'd eaten it several times, but never by itself. I had never cooked it before either. *Chef Leel's Perfect Wild Rice* combines nature's original rice with the perfect balance of spices and herbs.

Procedure:
1. Strain and rinse soaked wild rice with distilled or spring water. Combine wild rice and 8 cups spring water in a pot.
2. Bring to a boil. Cover and reduce heat, Simmer on lo for 55-65 minutes, or until the rice has curled. Stir occasionally.
3. Remove from heat. Add remaining ingredients to rice and mix well. Leave covered. Let cool. Serve. Enjoy.

Chef Leel's Perfect Wild Rice pairs well with *Chef Leel's Chicken Fried Mushrooms*, soups, and pasta. Pair it with any of your favorite meals to add depth. *Chef Leel's Wild Rice* can be used to make plant sushi, mock burgers, veggie fritters, and more.

Chef Leel's Cheazy Kamut Pasta

Servings:
Serves 2-4

Equipment:
Saucepot   Pasta strainer
Mixing spoon

Ingredients:

2 cups Kamut elbows
4 cups spring water
1/2 tsp sea salt
2 cups *Chef Leel's Brazil Nut Cheddar*

There's always a particular traditional family dish that you can identify just from the smell. Whether you're in your room with the door closed or entering your home from the opposite end of the kitchen, The aroma of certain dishes seduces your senses. In my family, one of those dishes was mac & cheese. We often kept it quick and simple, composing the mac & cheese the Velveeta way, adding our own twist to it. *The Chef Leel Way* takes that cheazy adventure and uses complementary ingredients that provide a healthy, in-house variation you and your family will enjoy.

Procedure:
1. Add 4 cups of spring water to a pot. Bring to a boil.
2. Add Kamut elbows to boiling water. Bring to boil. Reduce heat to rolling boil. Cover. Cook for 10-12 minutes or until tender.
3. Remove from heat. Transfer to a pasta strainer. Return to pot and mix in sea salt.
4. Pour over and fold in *Chef Leel's Brazil Nut Cheddar* to cooked pasta. Serve immediately or cover and let cool. Enjoy.

Chef Leel's Cheazy Kamut Pasta is a great addition to any dinner. You can enjoy this on the side of *Chef Leel's Chicken Fried Mushrooms* with a side salad. Of course this is the perfect dish to be enjoyed exclusively.

Chef Leel's Kamut Alfredo

Servings:
Serves 2-4

Equipment:
Saucepot   Pasta strainer
Skillet   Mixing spoon

Ingredients:
4 cups kamut spirals
8 oz. king oyster mushrooms
1 tsp onion powder
3/4 tsp sea salt
1/4 tsp basil
1/4 tsp oregano
1/8 tsp african bird pepper
1 green bell pepper (sliced)
Chef Leel' s Brazil Nut Alfredo Sauce

Chef Leel's Kamut Alfredo takes me back to several different events on my journey. I can recall my childhood, the first time I had pasta with alfredo sauce. That's the type of pasta style that keeps you coming back for seconds and thirds. Back at the HBCU, I can remember my friends and classmate throwing BBQs. The only food that didn't touch the grill was that pasta with the alfredo sauce. It's one of those satisfying dishes that almost anyone can compose. When you prepare your alfredo pasta, *The Chef Leel Way*, you utilize veggies, herbs, and grains to build a bowl of nutritious deliciousness.

Procedure:
1. Slice mushrooms into half circles, quarter-inch thick.
2. Preheat skillet to medium heat. Add bell pepper slices with minimal oil. Cook for 5 minutes.
3. Add mushrooms and dry ingredients excluding 1/2 tsp sea salt and 1/2 tsp onion powder. Stir fry for 5 minutes. Remove from heat.
4. Cook kamut spirals according to package. Strain. Mix in remaining dry ingredients.
5. Combine all ingredients in a pot. Serve warm. Enjoy,

Chef Leel's Kamut Alfredo is an all-in-one pasta satisfaction. *Chef Leel's Kamut Alfredo* is a versatile dish. Try adding in different sauteed veggies or mushrooms, or topping it with *Chef Leel's Plum Tomato Sauce*.

Chef Leel's Chicken Fried Mushrooms

Servings:
Serves 2-4

Equipment:
Whisk   Mixing Bowl (x2)
Tongs   Paper Towel
Small Pan

Ingredients:
6 oz. oyster mushrooms
3 cups garbanzo flour
4 tsp onion powder
3 tsp sea salt
1 tsp basil
1 tsp oregano
1/2 tsp ginger
1 cup spring water
1/2 cup avocado oil

It's no mystery that chicken is at the center of the standard American diet, especially fried chicken. We all crave for that crisp, crunchy seasoned skin and meaty, tender flesh. Throughout my childhood years, fried chicken was a staple. I never knew how my mom, my aunts or uncles, or grandma made this staple dish. I was only concerned with the final product. We would dip it in ranch or barbecue sauce and eat to our heart's content. With *Chef Leel's Chicken Fried Mushrooms*, you get all the flavor, crunch, and tenderness without any of the residual effects of consuming chicken.

Procedure:

1. Add half of all dry ingredients into two separate bowls. Add 1 cup spring water to one of the bowls. Whisk until fully combined.
2. Separate mushrooms leaving stems attached. Larger mushrooms have more depth.
3. Dip mushrooms in wet batter, then into dry batter.
4. Preheat pan to medium-hi. Add avocado oil and allow it to heat up.
5. Gently place 3-4 breaded mushrooms in pan. Fry until brown. Flip and fry until golden brown.
6. Transfer to paper towel lined surface. Serve and Enjoy.

Chef Leel's Chicken Fried Mushrooms are complementary to just about any dish. You can wrap them in *Chef Leel's Spelt Tortillas* or have them in a small bowl with a side of *Chef Leel's Hempseed Ranch*.

Chef Leel's Raw Garden Salad

Servings:
Serves 1-2

Equipment:
Salad Bowl   Whisk   Knife
Fork   Container with lid

Ingredients:
1 head green leaf lettuce
2 plum tomatoes (sliced)
1/2 yellow bell pepper (diced)
1/2 red onion (diced)
1 small avocado (sliced)
8 oz. baby bella mushrooms
(marinated)

Mushroom Marinade:
1 tbsp sesame oil
1 tbsp spring water
1 1/2 tsp sea salt
1/2 tsp onion powder
1/4 tsp basil
1/4 tsp oregano
1/4 tsp thyme
Pinch fennel

After a long day of work or school, a satisfying meal is necessary. The task of composing a quality meal after having exerted so much energy can be inconvenient. We tend to have fully-cooked dinners to conclude our fruitful days. Other times, we don't think twice before stopping for fast food or ordering a quick take-out meal to fulfill our hunger. When you're ready to eat, the procedure of preparing or cooking a meal can be tedious. *Chef Leel's Raw Garden Salad* is the no-cook alternative that provides the raw nutrients of each ingredient. Enjoy a quick, easy, fulfilling salad, *The Chef Leel Way*.

Procedure:
1. Prepare marinade in a bowl or container. Add all marinade ingredients, whisk until fully combined.
2. Slice mushrooms and add to marinade. Fully incorporate marinade by gently folding in mushrooms. Cover with lid or plastic wrap. Allow marinating for at least 45 minutes at room temperature.
3. In a salad bowl, add green leaf lettuce, plum tomatoes, bell peppers, onion, and marinate mushrooms. Lastly, add avocado. Top avocado with key lime juice to prolong freshness.
4. Serve with *Chef Leel's Alkaline Island Dressing* or *Chef Leel's Hempseed Ranch*. Enjoy.

Chef Leel's Raw Garden Salad is a complete meal by itself. A smaller portion can be made to be eaten as an appetizer. The marinated mushrooms can also be substituted for *Chef Leel's Chicken Fried Mushrooms* for a more dynamic experience.

Chef Leel's Plum Tomato Sauce

Ingredients:

10 plum tomatoes (quarter cut)
1/2 tbsp onion powder
1 1/4 tsp sea salt
1/2 tsp dried basil
1/8 tsp african bird pepper
1 tbsp fresh oregano

Servings:
Yields 20-28oz

Equipment:
Blender   Sauce Pot
Mixing Spoon

Procedure:

1. Add all ingredients to blender. Pulse 3-4 times.
2. Blend on high for 30 seconds (2x).
3. Transfer mixture to a small saucepot and bring to boil. Reduce heat. Simmer uncovered for 20 minutes or until desired consistency is reached. Stir occasionally.
4. Use immediately or allow to cool and transfer to a glass container and store in refrigerator.

Chef Leel's Plum Tomato Sauce is a great addition to pasta, pizzas, and can even be used as a dipping sauce.

Chef Leel's Brazil Nut Alfredo Sauce

Ingredients:

1 cup Brazil nuts (soaked overnight)
1 tsp sea salt 2 tbsp *Sea Moss Gel*
1 tsp onion powder 1 1/2 cups spring water
1/4 tsp ginger
1/4 tsp basil
2 tsp grapeseed oil

Servings:

Yields 16-20oz

Equipment:

Blender   Sauce Pot
Mixing Spoon

Procedure:

1. Add all ingredients to blender. Blend on high for 30 seconds (2x).
2. Transfer mixture to small saucepot and bring to a light boil. Simmer uncovered for 2 minutes. Stir moderately.
3. Use immediately or allow to cool and transfer to a glass container and store in refrigerator,

Chef Leel's Brazil Nut Alfredo Sauce pairs well with Italian-style dishes, including pasta, pizza, and lasagna.

Chef Leel's Brazil Nut Cheddar

Ingredients:
3/4 cup Brazil nuts (soaked overnight)
1/4 cup hemp seeds
1 orange bell pepper (chopped)
1 tsp sea salt
1 tsp onion powder
1/4 tsp ginger
1 key lime juice
1 cup spring water

Servings:
Yields 16-20 oz

Equipment:
Blender
Sauce Bottle

Procedure:
1. Add all ingredients to blender. Blend on low for 10 seconds.
2. Blend on high for 30 seconds.
3. Use immediately or transfer to a glass jar or sauce bottle and store in refrigerator.

Chef Leel's Brazil Nut Cheddar is a great substitute for traditional cheese. You can add *Chef Leel's Brazil Nut Cheddar* to pastas, pizzas, wraps, and even salads.

Chef Leel's Alkaline Island Dressing

Ingredients:
1/2 cup hemp seeds
1/4 tsp basil
1/2 cup spring water
1/8 tsp achiote
2 cherry tomatoes
2 medjool dates (pitted)
1 tsp sea salt
1/2 tsp onion powder
1/4 tsp african bird pepper
1 key lime juice

Servings:
Yields 12-16 oz

Equipment:
Blender
Sauce Bottle

Procedure:
1. Dice cherry tomatoes.
2. Add all ingredients to blender. Pulse 3-4 times.
3. Blend on high for 30 seconds.
4. Use immediately or transfer to a glass jar or sauce bottle and store in refrigerator.

Chef Leel's Alkaline Island Dressing can be massaged into any of your favorite salads. Also, try using this as a dip for your favorite raw veggies and appetizers.

Chef Leel's Hemp Seed Ranch

Ingredients:
3/4 cup hemp seeds
1/2 tsp sea salt
1/2 tsp onion powder
1/8 tsp dill
1 key lime juice
5/8 cup spring water

Servings:
Yields 12-16 oz

Equipment:
Blender
Sauce Bottle

Procedure:
1. Add all ingredients to blender.
2. Blend on high for 30 seconds.
3. Use immediately or transfer to a glass jar or sauce bottle and store in refrigerator.

Chef Leel's Hempseed Ranch is the ultimate dipping sauce and dressing for salad. Try pairing this dairy free ranch with *Chef Leel's Chicken Fried Mushrooms.*

Chef Leel's Hemp Seed Mayo

Ingredients:
1 cup hemp seeds
1 tsp onion powder
1/2 tsp sea salt
1/4 tsp ginger
1/2 key lime juice
2 tbsp olive oil
5/8 cup spring water

Servings:
Yields 8 oz

Equipment:
Blender
Glass Jar

Procedure:
1. Add all ingredients to blender.
2. Blend on low for 20 seconds. Increase speed to high. Blend for 30 seconds.
3. Use immediately or transfer to a glass jar or sauce bottle and store in refrigerator.

Chef Leel's Hemp Seed Mayo is a nutritionally dense spread made for sandwiches and wraps. Try mixing this mayo with other sauces to create different flavors and textures.

Chef Leel's Spelt Tortillas

Servings:
Yields 6-8 tortillas

Equipment:
Mixing bowl   Rolling pin
Plastic wrap   Skillet
Kitchen towel

Ingredients:
2 cups white spelt flour
1 tsp sea salt
2 tbsp grapeseed oil
3/4 cup spring water

Quick meals are usually repetitive to make up for the time we need to tend to other tasks and to ease the effort of composing a meal that is fulfilling. Mexican-style dishes like hard-shell tacos, soft-shell tacos, and burritos were easy go-to's in our family. These were dishes that didn't take too much time to make and were always exciting to eat. White or cornflour tortillas made these dishes possible. We would also use the tortillas to build our own snacks and wraps. *Chef Leel's Spelt Tortillas* allow you to throw out the bleached flour tortillas and build your own with one of nature's ancient grains so you can roll up and wrap your favorite combinations of veggies.

Procedure:
1. In a mixing bowl, combine flour, salt, and oil. Mix in 1/2 cup water.
2. Gradually add remaining water. Form into a ball. Knead for 3 minutes. Cover and allow to rest for 2 minutes.
3. Preheat pan to medium. Cut into 8 equal parts. Roll into 8 inch tortillas or desired length.
4. Place tortilla in preheated skillet. Allow bubbles to form. Flip and cook for 30 seconds or until all moisture has receded.
5. Place finished tortillas on kitchen towel and fold over to cover or cover with additional towel.

Chef Leel's Spelt Tortillas are soft, light, and pliable, and are delectable shells you can use to customize wraps with your favorite veggies and fillings.

Chef Leel's Spelt Tortilla Chips

Servings:
Serves 2-4

Equipment:
Mixing bowl   Rolling Pin
Baking Sheet   Pasta Cutter
Wheel

Ingredients:
2 cups white spelt flour
1 tsp sea salt
2 tbsp grapeseed oil
3/4 cup spring water

Transitioning into a healthier lifestyle would require one to be more authoritative over the foods they consume. This includes processed foods and snacks. All my life, snacks have been mandatory in my daily regimen of food. Whenever I was doing homework or watching a movie, I loved having a bag of chips to munch on. I preferred certain flavors, but the most important feature of a chip was its crunch. Combining the crunch of a chip with a dip was the innovation of eating a delicious bag of chips all by itself. *Chef Leel's Spelt Tortilla Chips* are the homemade snack that satisfies a midday craving and are versatile enough to be paired with any dip.

Procedure:

1. Preheat oven to 350°F. In a mixing bowl, combine flour, salt, and oil. Mix in 1/2 cup water.
2. Gradually add remaining water. Form into a ball. Knead for 3 minutes. Cover and allow to rest for 2 minutes.
3. Cut into 2 equal parts and roll out very thin.
4. Apply a thin layer of oil to baking sheet. Transfer dough to sheet. Cut into triangles or desired shapes.
5. Bake for 13 minutes on bottom rack. Check occasionally. Remove from oven. Serve immediately or allow to cool. Enjoy.

Chef Leel's Spelt Tortilla Chips are light and crunchy and are a great snack for any time of the day. Nothing compares to the experience of taking a bite of *Chef Leel's Electric Guac* with these chips.

Sea Moss Gel

Ingredients:
2 oz sea moss (dried)
10 cups spring water

Servings:
Yields 20 oz

Equipment:
Medium Bowl
Blender

Procedure:
1. Cover 2 oz dried sea moss in 8 cups spring water overnight.
2. Strain and discard water.
3. Add reconstituted sea moss and 2 cups spring water to blender.
4. Pulse 5 times. Blend on high for 30 seconds (2x).
5. Transfer to glass jar. Use immediately or store in refrigerator.

Sea Moss Gel can be eaten raw, added to teas, water, juices, or smoothies, or used as a cooking oil replacement.

Chef Leel's Sea Moss Smoothie

Ingredients:
5 baby bananas
1/8 tsp anise
5 medjoul dates (pitted)
1 pinch sea salt
2 cups spring water
2 tbsp sea moss gel
3/4 cups walnuts (soaked overnight)
1/4 cup hemp seeds

Servings:
Yields 24 oz

Equipment:
Blender
Single Serve Cup

Procedure:
1. Add baby bananas, medjoul dates, spring water, and *Sea Moss Gel* to blender.
2. Add remaining ingredients to blender. Blend on low for 15 seconds
3. Blend on high for 45 seconds.
4. Transfer to a single-serve cup and enjoy immediately or store in refrigerator.

Chef Leel's Sea Moss Smoothie is the perfect breakfast smoothie or lunch replacement. You can also consume this as a pre or post-workout drink.

Chef Leel's Very Berry Smoothie

Ingredients:
1 cup blackberries
1 cup blueberries
1/2 cup raspberries
2 medjoul dates (pitted)
1/2 avocado
1 cup spring water

Servings:
Yields 20-24 oz

Equipment:
Blender
Single Serve Cup

Procedure:
1. Add all ingredients to blender.
2. Blend on high for 30 seconds.
3. Transfer to glass jar or single-serve cup. Serve. Enjoy.

Chef Leel's Very Berry Smoothie is great for jump-starting your day, or even as refreshment before a meal.

Chef Leel's Black Tahini Frosting

Ingredients:
10 medjoul dates (pitted)
1/4 cup ground black sesame
seeds
2 cups spring water

Servings:
Yields 16-22 oz

Equipment:
Blender
Glass Jar

Procedure:
1. Add all ingredients to blender. Pulse 4-6 times.
2. Blend on a medium speed for 30 seconds. Blend on high for another 15-30 seconds or until smooth
3. Use immediately or transfer to a glass jar and store in refrigerator.

Chef Leel's Black Tahini Frosting is perfect on top of *Chef Leel's Brownie Cakes.* This frosting will also pair well with any of your favorite homemade vegan pastries.

Chef Leel's Electric Brownie Cakes

Servings:
Yields 18 pieces

Equipment:
Mixing Spoon   Mixing Bowl
Whisk   Brownie Pan

Ingredients:
2 cups teff flour
3/4 cup ground black sesame seeds
1 tsp sea salt
1/2 cup date sugar
1/2 cup grapeseed oil
1/2 cup raw blue agave
1 cup sparkling water
1/3 cup walnuts (chopped)

Grandma's cakes, pastries, and pies were always homemade and in high demand. Having her sweet snacks throughout the day or between meals felt almost like it was necessary to function as a child, growing teenager, and young adult. What was even more satisfying was having a savory meal, then having dessert to follow it up. Sometimes the most exciting time for sweets was right before bed. Even so, most desserts contain dairy and animal byproducts, processed sugars, and unhealthy fats. *Chef Leel's Electric Brownie Cakes* are cruelty free, light and rich sweet treats you can enjoy anytime.

Procedure:
1. Preheat oven to 350°F.
2. Add dry ingredients to mixing bowl. Whisk well to combine.
3. Add oil, agave, and sparkling water to dry batter. Fold in wet ingredients until mixture is fully combined.
4. Transfer mixture to brownie pan. Bake for 15 minutes.
5. Remove from oven. Gently spread over an even layer of *Chef Leel's Black Tahini Frosting.*
6. Return to oven and bake for 15 minutes or until a toothpick comes out clean.
7. Remove from oven. Allow to cool or serve warm. Cut evenly into 18 pieces or desired sections. Enjoy.

Chef Leel's Electric Brownie Cakes are delectable treats suitable for any occasion. Satisfy your sweet tooth after a savory meal, or enjoy these as your end of the day sweet reward.

MEAL
CREATIVITY

Meal ideas using *Veginners* recipes

Maximizing your experience:
- Create meals by combining components of different recipes.
  - Use one recipe as the main dish and others as side dishes.
  - Substitute one approved pasta for another.
  - Mix, match, and exchange condiments. Interchange nuts and seeds in recipes.
  - Turn breakfast into brunch. Turn pancakes into waffles.
  - For recipes that include batter or breading, incorporate either or both to create new dish styles and flavors.
  - African bird pepper can always be exchanged for cayenne pepper.
- Substitute different flours for corresponding recipes.
  - You can use other glutenous flours like white spelt, kamut, white kamut, or rye flour for a recipe that calls for spelt flour. You could also experiment with gluten-free flours like garbanzo bean, amaranth, quinoa, or teff flour.
- Mushrooms are pervasive and interchangeable.
  - Mushrooms may be more or less accessible. Most edible mushrooms can be substituted with almost any other. Be excited to substitute oyster mushrooms with white mushrooms; you'll enjoy a new experience.
- Greens grow in a variety and have different textures at different stages.
  - In a recipe that calls for raw kale, you can exchange it for lettuce. Mature kale can also be interchanged with baby kale. One green can be exchanged for another.

-Chef Leel's Chicken Fried Mushrooms
-Baked butternut squash
-Kale salad
-Avocado
-Chef Leel's Hempseed Ranch

Chef Leel's Spelt Tortillas-
Chef Leel's Alkaline Island Dressing-
Green leaf lettuce-
Orange bell peppers-
Red onions-
Marinated mushrooms *(p.34)-*

-Kamut spirals
-*Chef Leel's Plum Tomato Sauce*
-Sauteed bell pepper and onions
-*Chef Leel's Ground Shroom*
-*Chef Leel's Brazil Nut Cheddar*

Baby Kale-
Chef Leel's Perfect Quinoa-
Sauteed yellow onions-
Zucchini-
Baked portobello mushrooms-
Sesame seeds-
Chef Leel's Alkaline Island Dressing-

-*Chef Leel's Spelt Tortillas*
-Assorted bell peppers
-White onions
-Diced plum tomatoes
-*Chef Leel's Ground Shroom*
-*Chef Leel's Guac*
-*Chef Leel's Hempseed Ranch*

Turnip greens-
Chef Leel's Perfect Wild Rice-
Baked kabocha squash-
Pan-grilled oyster mushrooms-
Chef Leel's Cheazy Kamut Pasta-

Important Things to Remember

- If a food is not listed in this Nutritional Guide, it is NOT recommend.
- Drink one gallon of natural spring water daily.
- Take Dr. Sebi's products one hour prior to pharmaceuticals.
- All of Dr. Sebi's products may be taken together with no interaction.
- Following the Nutritional Guide strictly and taking the products regularly, produces the best results with reversing disease.
- No animal products, no dairy, no fish, no hybrid foods and no alcohol.
- Natural growing grains are alkaline-based; it is recommended that you consume only the grains listed in the Nutritional Guide instead of wheat.
- Many of the grains listed in the Nutritional Guide are available as pastas, bread, flour or cereal and can be purchased at better health food stores.
- Dr. Sebi's products are still releasing therapeutic properties 14 days after being taken.
- Dr. Sebi says, "Avoid using a microwave, it will kill your food."
- Dr. Sebi says, "No canned or seedless fruits."

Vegetables

- Amaranth greens (Callaloo, a variety of greens)
- Avocado
- Bell Peppers
- Chayote (Mexican squash)
- Cucumber
- Dandelion greens
- Garbanzo beans
- Izote (Cactus flower/cactus leaf)
- Kale
- Lettuce (All, except Iceberg)
- Mushrooms (All, except Shitake)
- Nopales (Mexican cactus)

- Okra
- Olives
- Onions
- Sea Vegetables (Wakame/dulse/arame/hijiki/nori)
- Squash
- Tomato (Cherry and plum only)
- Tomatillo
- Turnip greens
- Zucchini
- Watercress
- Purslane (Verdolaga)
- Wild arugula

Fruits

- Apples
- Bananas (The smallest one or the Burro/midsize/original banana)
- Berries (All varieties, no cranberries)
- Elderberries (In any form)
- Cantaloupe
- Cherries
- Currants
- Dates
- Figs
- Grapes (Seeded)
- Limes (Key limes, with seeds)
- Mango

- Melons (Seeded)
- Orange (Seville or sour preferred, difficult to find)
- Papayas
- Peaches
- Pears
- Plums
- Prickly Pear (Cactus fruit)
- Prunes
- Raisins (Seeded)
- Soft Jelly Coconuts
- Soursops (Latin or West Indian markets)
- Tamarind

Natural Herbal Teas

- Burdock
- Chamomile
- Elderberry
- Fennel
- Ginger
- Raspberry
- Tila

Grains

- Amaranth
- Fonio
- Kamut
- Quinoa
- Rye
- Spelt
- Tef
- Wild Rice

Nuts & Seeds
(Including Nut & Seed Butters)

- Hemp Seeds
- Raw Sesame Seeds
- Raw Sesame "Tahini" Butter
- Walnuts
- Brazil Nuts

Oils

- Olive Oil (Do not cook)
- Coconut Oil (Do not cook)
- Grapeseed Oil
- Sesame Oil
- Hempseed Oil
- Avocado Oil

Mild Flavors

- Basil
- Bay leaf
- Cloves
- Dill
- Oregano
- Savory
- Sweet Basil
- Tarragon
- Thyme

Pungent & Spicy Flavors

- Achiote
- Cayenne/ African Bird Pepper
- Coriander (Cilantro)
- Onion Powder
- Habanero
- Sage

Salty Flavors

- Pure Sea Salt
- Powdered Granulated Seaweed
- (Kelp/Dulse/Nori – has "sea taste")

Sweet Flavors

- Pure Agave Syrup (From cactus)
- Date Sugar

60513560R00033